D1572054

WOLF!

**Wolves in American Culture Committee
Boise, Idaho**

Box 128
Ashland, WI 54806

ISBN 0-942802-15-2

Library of Congress Catalog Card Number
86-63259

About the Wolves and Humans Exhibit, the Wolves in American Culture Committee, and "**Wolf!**":

Minnesota has a long history of wolf-human relationships. Thus when biologist Curtis Hadland decided to develop the Wolves and Humans Exhibit at The Science Museum of Minnesota, he found expert colleagues in the area willing to help with the project. He called on world-famous wolf biologist L. David Mech, folklorist Ellen Stekert, wolf historian/naturalist Karlyn Atkinson-Berg, biologist Fred Harrington, and many other consultants and Museum staff members. Working as a team, these dedicated people developed **Wolves and Humans***, which has been seen by over one million visitors in Yellowstone National Park, Boise (Idaho), Boston, and New York, and will continue its tour in major American and Canadian cities for the next several years. Karlyn Atkinson-Berg also assembled a teacher's packet to enhance the educational value of the tour.* **Wolves and Humans** *was produced by the Science Museum of Minnesota with major support from The National Endowment for the Humanities.*

After a highly successful opening run in Yellowstone National Park, the Science Museum brought **Wolves and Humans** *to Idaho in 1985. Viewing the exhibit in Boise, U.S. Fish and Wildlife Service ecologist James Nee envisioned an anthology which would summarize past relationships between humans and wolves and describe present efforts to prove that these two species can co-exist in selected areas with mutual security and benefits. Nee consulted with USFWS Endangered Species specialist Jay Gore and other area biologists, then brought his idea to Boise State University, where he enlisted an editorial board consisting of professors Alan Brinton (Philosophy) and Orvis Burmaster (English), journalist Glenn Oakley (News Service), designer Janice Pavlic (Printing and Graphics Service), and writer-editor Barbara Simler (student intern). Nee, the editorial board, and fiscal officer Jo Ann Cole formed the Wolves in American Culture Committee, and applied to the Idaho Humanities Council for a grant to help produce this volume. The grant was awarded and, after a long and uneasy gestation period,* "**Wolf!**" *was born.*

Contents

STEPHEN R. KELLERT

Foreword

E veryone knows the Big Bad Wolf, but only a few of us know *Canis lupus*. The symbolic wolf retains its power to intimidate and obsess, even if its real counterpart remains somewhat obscure and impotent. Indeed, sometimes one is left wondering if Americans are more content with the image and the shadow than the tangible creature. Certainly the problems seem simpler, the costs and inconveniences of management and coexistence with the wolf infinitely less, when we deal merely with the mythic. Nurtured on a nearly continuous diet of vicarious experience through the media of books, films, and television, our literate society often seems satisfied with the mere appearance of reality.

The crucial question, however, is whether or not we have talked enough about the biological, social, economic, and psychological complexities of the wolf-human relationship to proceed wisely with reintroduction and management of wolves. Are we willing to confront the deeply-ingrained antipathy toward wolves which we find among rural, and especially among resource-dependent populations? And are we prepared to defend the notion that the ecological and ethical values of a wolf population are somehow translatable into tangible benefits at least equivalent if not superior to those offered by our present extraction of resources from a wolfless environment? Our discussions of the symbolic wolf will be justified only when we have convinced ourselves that we must move beyond the image and deal with the real animal.

The conflicting and enigmatic images of the wolf are vividly described by Glenn Oakley in his introductory chapter, "Historical Overview." The diversity of these images was also dramatically revealed to us in a recently-conducted study of public reactions to the timberwolf in Minnesota. Farmers, hunters, trappers, and other residents of the northern Minnesota wilderness, as well as urbanites of the Twin Cities, expressed a remarkable panoply of conflicting and confusing attitudes toward the wolf. Both Oakley's chapter and our research suggest that we need to consider these diverse views in our planning and educational activities, and that we probably must accept the intrinsic confusion and resistance as a price to be paid for a controversial, though courageous, act.

"The many wolves of folklore" described by Ellen Stekert will remain with us despite our educational efforts toward public awareness. And perhaps this is not entirely lamentable: Paul Shepard once remarked that we continue to need the wolf and other animals as much to think about as to live with. We can only hope that the wolf will move beyond being a scapegoat figure in our negative myths and legends and come to be seen as a useful figure in our literature and our culture.

The chapters on wolves in children's stories and in American Indian culture, by Judith Levin and Jeannette Ross, provide powerful additional testimony to the wolf's hold on our collective imagination. Both of these chapters suggest the possibility of our seeing the real animal and recognizing its potential for co-existence with *Homo sapiens*. David Mech further reinforces this possibility as he helps us to render the mythical somewhat mundane by understanding its simple biological functions of feeding, reproducing, and socializing. Mech's chapter on biology of the wolf has the curious effect of reducing the wolf to the level of mere creature and at the same time appealing to our sympathy as we watch it struggle for survival in an environment dominated by hostile humans.

The wolf, as this booklet amply attests, continues to function as a symbolic fulcrum upon which some of our most confused and contentious feelings toward the natural world are focused. Why all this fuss and bother about one single animal in the vast spectrum of species surviving precariously today? Because the wolf, in effect, offers a kind of litmus test of our willingness to change fundamentally and unequivocally our historic relationship to the natural world.

Curious that I should be writing this foreword from an apartment in Tokyo, the world's most populous city, where I have been conducting a comparative study of the Japanese and American perceptions of wildlife and nature. Perhaps it appropriately expresses the sadness the

Japanese people are now experiencing at having lost, in their feverish pursuit of modernity, a traditional reverence for nature. The Japanese have only recently begun to re-discover that the symbolic and historic are insufficient substitutes for the fundamentally meaningful experience of the real. How ironic that they now view Americans enviously for the value and variety of our relationships with nature. Perhaps our willingness to act boldly and benevolently on behalf of the Yellowstone wolf will signify not only a commitment to our fellow countrymen, but also to a world standing on the brink of irretrievably losing so much of its wild fauna. Certainly this booklet and the effort it represents symbolizes one of those rare opportunities to assert man's compatibility and compassionate relationship with nature.

Stephen R. Kellert
Tokyo, Japan
June, 1986

Stephen R. Kellert is a professor of forestry and environmental studies at Yale University.

GLENN OAKLEY

Historical Overview

I magine that you are walking alone through the woods. The fresh-fallen snow squeaks beneath your boots as you move along, following the meanders of a small stream. From beneath a tangle of brier a snowshoe hare dashes, bounds 20 yards and stops. Bemused, you pause to watch the hare, its black nose twitching. And then you hear it: the slow rising howl of wolves.

What is that sound to you? Is it the chilling call of a pack of dangerous killers, a cause for alarm? Or is it the joyous singing of one of Earth's most fascinating creatures? For many Americans the howl of wolves is a fearful sound. It is a sound that echoes through generations bred on belief in a wolf that is evil incarnate.

Wolves prowl through our subconscious: red-eyed, devious, conspiratorial wolves that kill to satiate their lust. Soulless demons pursuing horse-drawn sleighs through the dark winter forest.

These wolves of our Anglo-American cultural mind may have little in common with the wolves that live and die, largely unseen, in the northern forests and tundra. But centuries of legends, myths, stories, art and belief in a wolf that is the physical embodiment of evil are not easily dispelled.

"The Werewolves," 1865.

1

How we perceive the wolf usually says more about our own human culture than about *Canis lupus* itself. For several thousand years we of Old World descent have been an agrarian people for whom the wolf was an economic, physical and spiritual threat.

It is probable that our earliest ancestors—those stone age hunters of Europe—regarded wolves with respect. We know that the North American hunters—the Indian tribes of woodlands and plains—held the wolf in high esteem, imitating its hunting techniques, seeking its power.

And we know that far beyond human memory the early people tamed wolves. They may have captured wolf pups as pets, or perhaps for food. Wolves scavenging human camps may have become increasingly accustomed to the presence of people and become part of the camp. However it was accomplished, the two predators—man and wolf—formed an alliance and the course was set for the breeding of the first

"Through the woods"
T.J. Lawson '95

domestic animal. Man's best friend. Ironically, several thousand years later mankind would breed dogs specifically for the hunting and killing of wolves.

As the pack hunting instinct of wolves remains in domestic dogs, human respect and even admiration for the wolf has run a thin and intermittent thread through European and American culture.

Respect for the wolf is evidenced in the story of Romulus and Remus, the Mowgli stories, and occasional fables that promote the wolf as the quintessence of freedom. Like American Indians, early Anglo-Saxon kings and nobles named themselves after wolves, thus associating themselves with the cunning and fierce fighting abilities of the animals. Lewis and Clark in their journals referred to the wolf as the "shepherd of the buffalo." But this image of the wolf has usually withered against the black image of the animal.

From Hunter to Herder

Our Anglo-American ancestors' attitudes towards the wolf began to change when their culture began to change—from hunter to herder and ploughman. The wolf was no longer fellow hunter, but a predator that could decimate a flock of sheep—a family's source of food, shelter and clothing—in a single night.

The wolf was enemy: killer of sheep, cattle, chickens. And killer of people too. Indeed, the European and Asian wolf seems to have been more aggressive than its North American counterpart. Stories of man-eating wolves—the Beast of Gevaudan, said to have killed more than 60 children in France in the mid 1700s; the tales of wolf packs terrorizing peasant villages in Russia—became both legend and myth.

But the notoriety of wolves has far exceeded the real extent of the wolves' depredations against humans. Other animals also have competed against and killed humans. Bears, for example, have killed both people and livestock. And while bears and other predators have been hunted and trapped for bounty and sport, none of these other animals have engendered the fear and loathing of wolves. There is no wolf counterpart to Smokey the Bear. The wolves of children's cartoons are not at all like Yogi Bear.

In Western culture, the wolf has usually been seen as much more than a large wild dog; it has served as a symbol for all that was dark, wild and uncontrollable.

Perhaps this is because the wolf, of all the carnivores, is most like us. Both wolves and humans traveled in small groups of extended families—wolf packs and tribal bands. Both wolves and humans are

---

"Through the Woods," by Terry J. Lawson, 1985.

highly individualistic, yet rely on group cooperation to survive. And the wolf is probably second only to man in its capacity to adapt to extremes of climate. Before the extermination campaigns against the wolf, it ranged from the deserts of Israel to the swamps of Florida and the frozen arctic of Siberia.

But man, unlike the wolf, left the wilderness and became civilized. The woods became foreign—and thus more frightening—as man moved away from the wilderness and began shaping and creating a new, more comfortable environment. The wilderness was something to be fought against and tamed—something to be made right with an axe and plow. This attitude developed into a religious fervor with the spread of Christianity.

Subdue and conquer the earth, the Bible admonished in Genesis. Wilderness was an imperfect, dark and unhallowed place that awaited improvement by man. Part of that improvement included the removal of the wilderness beasts. And no beast was more deserving of Christian wrath than the wolf. For the wolf had become a symbol of the Devil.

An ivory carving from 900 A.D., the "Rambona Diptych," depicts Christ on the cross above the wolf, symbolizing Jesus' victory over the pagan, wolf-borne Rome. The metaphors were plentiful. If the followers of Christ were lambs, then who but wolves were the anti-Christ? The human view of the wolf darkened further. Not only was the wolf a menace to farm and flock, a symbol of hostile wilderness, but the wolf was in concert with the Devil. Satan's servants changed from human form to wolf form—were-wolves.

The Europeans who came to America carried with them such beliefs and applied them with a terrifying vengeance. The English had just finished killing the last wolves in their Atlantic nation when America was first being colonized. By 1743 the

"Rambona Diptych," left panel, circa 900 A.D.

4

last wolf in Scotland would be killed and by 1776 the Irish would kill the final wolf on that island. The pastoral had finally defeated the wild.

Howling Wilderness

America's unimaginably vast expanse of forests, rivers and cloud shrouded mountains were viewed with fear and revulsion by these pastoralists. The metaphor most commonly applied was a "howling wilderness." The howl of wolves, well associated with the devil, underscored the unGod-like quality of this land. Cotton Mather in 1707 wrote of "the Evening Wolves, the rabid and howling Wolves of the Wilderness [which] would make . . . Havock among you, and not leave the Bones till the morning." An early Vermont historian, Samuel Williams, wrote in his book, **Native Animals**, "One of the most common and noxious of all our animals is the wolf . . . . This animal is extremely fierce, sanguinous and carniverous. When a number of them associate it is not for peace but for war and destruction." Everything found despicably wild in America was likened to the wolf: the howling wilderness, the native people. And all were summarily destroyed.

Bounties paid on dead wolves made killing the animals profitable as well as righteously rewarding. Wolf-killing campaigns of military proportion and style were mounted. Tons of strychnine were strewn across the western prairie. Buffalo hunters who had put themselves out of business by their deadly efficiency turned to killing wolves as a full time occupation. With the buffalo all but exterminated, the wolves turned frequently to killing livestock, and ranchers responded with a killing campaign that was unprecedented in its scale and violence. Wolves were captured, infected with mange and released into the wilds in the hopes that they would spread the parasite throughout the population. Wolf pups were dug from their dens and strangled. With hounds, traps, set guns and poison, wolves were exterminated from virtually the entire United States. Even in the national parks wolves were hunted, trapped and poisoned—as a favor to the good and innocent deer, elk and moose.

And when the wolf population was reduced to a handful of individuals these last remaining wolves were given names and hunted down like outlaws. There was Old Whitey, Old Three Toes, the Phantom Wolf, the Custer Wolf, and Lobo—the King of Currampaw. One hundred and fifty men had tried to kill Three Toes of Harding County, South Dakota, using traps, set guns, dogs and poison. The man who finally killed this "renegade" wolf had his picture taken with the dead animal and was awarded an engraved gold watch, courtesy of the local stockmen.

Fear and Wonder

To man the hunter the wolf was wise and noble and powerful. To man the farmer, herder, village dweller the wolf was fierce and evil. And to modern man, what is the wolf today?

It seems that the wolf has become an enigmatic combination which inspires both fear and wonder.

Only now, a half century after the last wolves were tracked down and killed, are we considering the possibility of allowing some wolves to return to the West. Peaceful coexistence between wolves and people has been successfully demonstrated in northern Minnesota. Many people are excited about the prospect of wolf howls returning to the remaining wilderness in America. But even today, when we have such control over the environment that entire mountains can be systematically leveled in search of minerals and the wildest rivers dammed and turned into reservoirs, the thought of wild wolves evokes anxiety and resentment among some people. It would be a mistake to believe that the slaughter of wolves in America is universally regretted today.

While proposals for the reintroduction of wolves into Yellowstone National Park and the reestablishment of wolves in Montana and Idaho have drawn widespread support—60 percent of Yellowstone Park visitors polled in 1985 agreed that "If wolves can't return to Yellowstone on their own, then we should put them back ourselves"—the plans have also drawn fire.

Public hearings on the wolf recovery plan for the northern Rockies, held in the farming, ranching and logging community of Grangeville, Idaho, revealed that the wolf of evil lives on in our society. A county commissioner speaking against wolves offered an anecdote that seemed to spring from the most popular of all the wolf fairytales. "A little girl was lost in the woods up in the Red River six years ago," she said. "But she spent the night in a hollow log and was found safe the next day. If there were wolves this may have had a sad ending." Said another man, "I don't feel it is right to turn the wolves loose on . . . children that walk to a bus as mine do."

The belief that wolves have no place in a Christian world was expressed by one couple who wrote, "We have the right to take our relatives and friends to see the beautiful mountains of Idaho without having to pack a rifle right into a picnic area, while we gaze at the beauty God has given us."

Other arguments reflect less a fear of wolves than a resentment of the animals, a belief that wolves are unfair competition and simply have no right to exist. One Idahoan writing against the reestablishment of wolves said, "You hunters—do you prefer wolves over deer? You are not allowed over one mature male deer a year—none out of season.

Wolves kill does and fawns every day all year long." Another justified the extermination of wolves—and the continued exclusion of the animals from the Rockies—by saying, "In the settlement of the West the wolf was destroyed because it was undesirable to human well being."

Well, what good is a wolf anyway? Are wolves desirable to human well being?

From an ecological viewpoint the reintroduction of wolves in Yellowstone Park and similar areas would be beneficial. The wolves could resume their ecological role as predators to thin the herds of elk, deer and bison. Without natural predators and protected from human hunting, these herds are subject to frequent starvation because of overpopulation and the consequent overgrazing. And while sport hunting prevents overpopulation of deer and elk outside park boundaries, biologists have determined that several wolf packs could once again roam the wilds of central Idaho and northern Montana without significantly harming the population of deer and elk.

But wolves do pose a management problem for wildlife agencies. Livestock depredation might occur. The wolves' impact on big game will have to be monitored. And some folks are presumably going to be scared to go into the woods.

But it may be that the very question "what good is a wolf?" is wrong. Perhaps we as people are beginning to realize that wild creatures do not need our justification to exist, that they have an inherent right to live. And that their existence is an enrichment to the world. And thus an enrichment to ourselves.

Glenn Oakley is a journalist living in Boise, Idaho. His articles and photographs have appeared in a wide variety of publications including **Backpacker, Defenders, National Wildlife, and Sierra**.

L. DAVID MECH

Biology

T he wolf is a large wild dog. Actually, it is the original dog. More than 12,000 years ago humans domesticated their "best friend" from the wolf. All dogs—from Chinese pugs to St. Bernards—descended from the wolf.

Wolves are the largest member of the dog family which also includes coyotes, foxes, jackals, dingoes, and other "canids." Adult female wolves weigh 50 to 100 pounds and males 60 to 120; a few individuals may weigh more. Most wolves stand tall, with long, slender legs and large blocky feet. Often the animals are at first mistaken for a deer. But close-up one can see that a wolf has a long furry tail, pointed ears, and a long narrowing muzzle. Generally a wolf's fur is a mottled gray, with black, brown, and whitish shadings on various parts of its body. In high arctic regions, most wolves tend to be white, and in southern Canada a high percentage are black, whereas wolves in the U.S. and Mexico are generally gray.

The main food of the wolf is other animals, usually large ones. Wolves usually catch and kill their own prey and, although they will eat almost any animal, their main prey are beavers, deer, caribou, mountain sheep, mountain goats, elk, moose, bison, and musk-oxen. To spend much time

"Adult Female Wolf Leaping Creek Below Beaver Dam," by Scot Stewart.

and energy catching mice or other small animals would be a waste in the long run.

Wolves will, however, take advantage of large temporarily available supplies of small prey such as fish or waterfowl, and they will also eat garbage, berries, and carcasses they find dead. In some areas wolves feed on cows, sheep, dogs, and other domestic animals. Each wolf requires about 2.5 pounds of food per day. On the average they eat about 5.5 pounds, and if they get a chance, they will eat as much as 13 pounds per day.

A single wolf can take even the largest prey if the animal is in poor enough condition. For example, one wolf in Sweden killed 8 adult moose and a calf during one winter. Usually wolves hunt in packs when after large prey.

The Hunt

Wolves hunt by traveling over a large area, using their eyesight and keen sense of smell. I have seen them detect a cow and twin calf moose a mile and a half away. When they find a prey animal, they may get together excitedly and wag tails. Different prey have different kinds of defense. Deer depend on their alertness, speed, and endurance to escape, whereas moose tend to stand their ground and defy the wolves; musk-oxen form a defensive wall or circle, protecting their rumps and facing the wolves with their formidable horns and hooves.

Whatever the defense, the wolves must strive to overcome it. For this they depend on their fine senses, their speed, and aggressiveness. Still, each kind of prey is also expert at applying its defenses. Thus, usually wolves and their prey are fairly evenly matched.

But if the prey has any serious weakness, it will then easily fall victim to the wolves. These weaknesses can vary considerably. For example, in any crop of young animals, some will be less vigorous than others; they will be more likely to fall prey to wolves. Or, as adult prey animals grow old, eventually they will become weaker and less able to defend themselves. Furthermore, if prey food conditions deteriorate, or extreme weather afflicts the prey, they will become easier for wolves to kill. And finally, if disease, parasites, injuries, or other factors harm the prey, wolves then have the advantage. In all these types of situations, biologists say the prey is "predisposed" to wolf predation.

Thus wolves are constantly faced with trying to find enough predisposed prey. To solve that problem, wolves must travel long and hard. Their usual rate of travel is about 5 miles per hour. When they do find prey, they can run up to 45 miles per hour. Usually, wolves

"Wolf Pups Howling," by Scot Stewart.

can tell quickly whether they can catch their prey or not, and if not, they give up within a few minutes. However, one Minnesota wolf was observed chasing and following a deer for 13 miles over a 4-hour period.

Because of their need to cover long distances to find enough prey, wolves inhabit large territories. Whereas prey animals generally live in only a few square miles and share an area together, wolves are highly territorial. The territory of a single pack is measured in tens, hundreds, or thousands of square miles, depending on the number of prey. Single wolves have covered as much as 1,600 square miles in one year.

Usually one wolf pack tries to keep other packs out of its territory. This reduces the competition for the pack's own prey and helps insure enough food for itself. Thus in the territory of one wolf pack there may be hundreds of prey animals upon which the pack prey. If neighboring packs try to intrude on the territory, the resident wolves chase them, fight them, and sometimes kill them.

Generally, however, wolves do not have to fight with neighbors because they have indirect ways of keeping outsiders away. Two such means are well known: howling and scent-marking. By howling as a group, wolves tell their neighbors where they are and warn them to stay out. Wolves also use their urine to say the same thing. By sprinkling urine like dogs do on conspicuous objects such as bushes, logs, snow clumps, rocks, etc., wolves leave signposts that may last for weeks. The two systems complement each other: howling tells where wolves

are at a given instant; scent-marking tells where wolves have been over a long period. Both mark the territory.

Pack Hierarchy

Each territory supports an entire pack of wolves, and a pack is really a family group. Each pack is headed by a set of parents, known as the "alpha pair." These individuals are the mature members of the pack, and the remaining members usually are their offspring. Offspring generally are produced each year, so pack members can be from the latest litter or from earlier ones. Offspring have been known to remain with a pack for as long as 4 years.

Among the members of a pack, there is a certain order. No pack member acts independently. Rather, the alpha male and alpha female guide the pack's activities, and the offspring follow their lead. Each animal's position in the social order is known to the other pack members and it remains constant for long periods. The alpha wolf of each sex dominates all the other members of the same sex. In large packs, there usually will also be a lowest ranking member of each sex, which is often picked on by its packmates. When interacting with another pack member a high ranking wolf tends to inflate its size by holding its ears erect, raising its mane, and holding its tail horizontal or straight up. Low ranking wolves do just the opposite: hold ears low, mane down, tail tucked between legs.

By constantly demonstrating their status this way, members maintain the pack order. As breeding season approaches, usually a 6-week period in late winter and spring, social competition increases. Nevertheless, usually the alpha pair holds its position and does the breeding, although sometimes two pairs may breed in a pack. The female comes into estrus (heat) for up to 15 days. When bred, she carries the pups for about 63 days. A week or so before the pups' birth, the female seeks a den, which may be a hole in the ground, a crack in a rockpile, a cave, hollow log, old beaver house, or some similar shelter. Often the same den is used each year. Wolves may keep the same mate for many years or may have two or more mates throughout their life.

A wolf's litter size can range up to 11, but about 6 is the average number of pups produced. The pups' eyes open at day 11 to 15, most puppy teeth are present in about week 3, and weaning takes place at about week 5. After about week 8, the pups are moved to a ground nest, where they romp and play over an area of up to an acre, an area known as a "rendezvous site." The pups may spend up to 3 weeks at one site but often are then shifted as far away as 5 miles to another. Probably depending on the degree of development of pups, they may continue this behavior even through winter. However, pups in good physical condition will join adult members of a pack in their travels as early as October. At this time they may weigh 60 pounds and be almost adult size. Adult teeth replace deciduous teeth between weeks 16 and 26.

Pups begin to mature at about 10 months of age, but full maturation requires about 5 years. The presence of maturing individuals in the pack (comparable in development to human teenagers) causes social tension. Depending on pack size, prey availability, and probably several other factors, some wolves leave the pack and strike out on their own (disperse) when as young as 10 months of age. However, most often they remain with the pack until about 16 to 24-months old, and some stay even longer. Occasionally, some offspring take over the breeding in the pack, and their parents leave.

The Lone Wolf

Both male and female offspring disperse, and become lone wolves. Males tend to travel farther. Some wolves merely move next door, find a member of the opposite sex, mate, and begin their own pack. However, others drift around the population, covering hundreds of square miles, until they find a vacant territory and mate. Then they settle down and start their pack. Still other dispersers tend to head in straight lines and may travel more than 500 miles before setting up a territory, and taking a mate.

If a wolf pack has no room for additional wolves, dispersers may drift around trying to stay out of the way of the pack. If caught, they will be chased and may be killed. However, if the wolf population still has room for more territories, the dispersers help keep its numbers high. Or they may spread the population beyond its borders into new areas.

Because of several "built-in" control features, wolf populations never really get as high as do most other wildlife populations. For example, deer can reach densities of 20 or more per square mile; coyotes and black bears are measured in numbers per 3 or 4 square miles. Wolves rarely reach more than one per 10 square miles over large areas, and more often wolf densities are measured in terms of wolves per 100 square miles. The reasons for this include the wolf pack's nature of holding very large territories, their failure to breed until 3 or more years old, and their tendency to restrict breeding to one or two females per pack.

Thus the wolf lives in relatively low numbers but has the ability of replenishing its populations readily. These characteristics tend to prevent wolves from eliminating their prey, yet they allow wolves to make quick use of whatever prey become vulnerable. Prey animals live in much higher densities, and each herd produces so many offspring that they usually can withstand wolf predation. The best example of these abilities comes from Isle Royale National Park in Lake Superior. There, wolves and moose have lived together without any human interference for 35 years. During a long period of favorable weather, the moose herd built up while wolf numbers remained the same. Then when the weather turned bad for several years, the wolves killed more moose and increased, moose numbers dropped, and eventually the wolves decreased. Now moose are recovering rapidly while wolf numbers have leveled off. In other areas where severe weather or heavy hunting by

"Typical full-size wolf track," by Robert Ream.

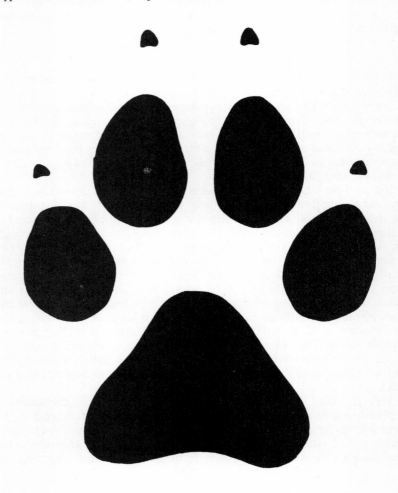

humans has reduced prey numbers, wolves have helped hold the prey down to low levels. This tendency has caused conflict with humans, so control of wolves has been advocated in such cases.

Another situation in which wolf control is asserted is when wolves kill domestic animals. For example, in Minnesota, many cattle and sheep farms are situated in wooded areas where wolves live. Ranchers often mistakenly place their dead animals out at the edge of their farms, and wolves feed on them. This practice keeps the wolves around the area, and may even teach wolves that livestock are good to eat.

Whatever the case, wolves do kill cattle and sheep in some cases, and the federal government then tries to destroy the offending wolves. In this way, the level of wolf predation on livestock is kept low. Generally, only about 11 farms out of 10,000 farms in wolf range have any trouble with wolves each year. Only about 5 cattle per 10,000 and 12 sheep per 10,000 in wolf range are claimed annually to have been killed by wolves.

It was just such competition with humans that caused the loss of wolves from most of the U.S., however. Originally wolves inhabited all of North America north of central Mexico. They were capable of surviving in any kind of natural habitat: desert, brushland, prairie, mountain, deciduous forest, boreal forest, swamp, marsh, tundra, and high arctic. As long as there was some kind of large prey in an area, wolves could live there.

Historically, biologists regarded wolves from various areas of North America as representing different races of one species, the gray wolf. Thus they applied names like arctic wolf, timber wolf, plains wolf, Mexican wolf, northern Rocky Mountain wolf, and so on, and these names are still used today. All these types of wolves can interbreed, and it is difficult for anyone except specialists to tell them apart. In the southeastern U.S. the wolf was represented by the "red wolf," which some people think is a different species. However, the red wolf is much the same as the gray wolf, and some biologists consider the red wolf to be merely another race of the gray wolf.

As European settlers tamed much of North America, they killed off many of the wolf's prey and substituted their own large animals: cattle, sheep, horses, pigs, goats, etc. Wolves then substituted these animals for their natural prey. But humans would not tolerate such competition, so they exterminated wolves from most of the U.S., part of southern Canada, and just about all of Mexico.

Every conceivable method was used to eliminate wolves: guns, traps, poisons, den-digging, bounties, and a wide variety of specialized techniques, many of which were highly inhumane. However, poison was the most effective method. During the anti-wolf campaign, cowboys carried poison, lacing every dead carcass. Government "wolfers" specialized in exterminating wolves. The effort was so effective that wolves were eliminated even from areas where they did not compete with livestock, including Yellowstone National Park.

The Wolf Today

Today the wolf inhabits only a small part of the contiguous U.S. and is considered an endangered species there except for Minnesota, where it is listed as threatened. Minnesota still supports about 1,200 wolves over a 30,000 square-mile area bordering Canada. Nearby Wisconsin contains 10 to 20 wolves, and Upper Michigan, perhaps 5 to 10; Isle Royale National Park in Lake Superior holds from 15 to 50. Glacier National Park and the adjacent Flathead National Forest in northwestern Montana currently contains approximately 15 wolves, and Idaho probably has less than half that number. All current wolf habitat is basically wilderness except part of the Minnesota and Wisconsin wolf range which is semi-wilderness.

Wolves still thrive in Canada and Alaska, which are largely unsettled. There are perhaps some 50,000 wolves throughout about 80% of their original range in Canada, and 5,000 to 7,500 in Alaska. In those areas wolf numbers are monitored by state and provincial game departments and generally are managed in much the same way as other wildlife. Wolf numbers are deliberately controlled in some areas of Canada and Alaska to help restore big game herds.

In the long run, it is the preservation of wilderness that will prove to be the single most important factor in insuring that wolves will survive. Without wilderness, wolves constantly get into trouble with humans by preying on domestic livestock and pets. Although wolves are sometimes killed by bears, and they suffer from a few diseases and parasites, their primary enemy by far is the irate human being. If we can preserve enough wilderness, wolves can continue to prey on large wild mammals and minimize competition with humans.

Because of society's recently awakened environmental awareness, the future looks good for the wolves remaining in North America. Certainly there will be no more extensive extermination campaigns, although local wolf control no doubt will continue from time to time. Intensive and long-term wolf studies have been underway in Isle Royale National Park, the Superior National Forest of Minnesota, and in Riding Mountain National Park, Manitoba. Endangered wolf populations in Wisconsin, Idaho, and Montana are being monitored.

Currently the federal government is even considering proposals for restoring wolves to certain areas. Yellowstone National Park and the Dare County peninsula in North Carolina (for red wolf) are two areas being seriously considered at present. Other possible candidate areas for wolf reintroduction could include central Idaho, the Adirondack Mountains of New York, and the Olympic Peninsula of Washington. Depending on how successful and popular these restorations were, other areas of the West could also be considered. Such restoration could be accomplished successfully as long as the public was willing to accept limited wolf control to minimize impacts of wolves on livestock.

Obviously the wolf can never again live in much of its original range. However, the knowledge and the technology now exist to help undo some of the damage an environmentally naive and exploitative society once wrought on wolves. If humans can understand that the wolf, with proper management, can fit back into wilderness ecosystems with minimal damage to human interests, everyone who enjoys the outdoors will be richer.

L. David Mech, Ph.D., is a research biologist for the U.S. Fish and Wildlife Service in St. Paul, Minnesota, and adjunct professor in ecology and behavorial biology at the University of Minnesota. He is a lecturer and the author of some 200 articles as well as three books, including **The Wolf: ecology and behavior of an endangered species.** *He was chief consultant to The Science Museum of Minnesota's* **Wolves and Humans** *exhibit.*

ELLEN J. STEKERT

Folklore

I once backpacked ten miles more than I intended on Isle Royale
lest I find myself in the area of the "wolf study" when it came time
to pitch my tent. We had all been told of the wildlife biologists' ex-
periments on the island. Had I dropped in on the researchers, I might
have met wolf biologist Dave Mech fifteen years earlier than our first
encounter in Minneapolis. But instead I made tracks as fast as I could
to the next camping area (ironically named after a mythical Native
American cannibal monster, Windigo). I was from the city; I had never
seen a wolf; so why was my apprehension so great that it prompted
me to action which resulted in considerable fatigue and impressive
blisters? A clue to the answer is in a sound track I heard the other night
as I watched a horror-sci-fi movie on TV—at the moment of greatest
danger one could discern, faint but distinct in the background, the howl
of a wolf. Our European-American folklore has taught us, in part, to
view the wolf as a life-threatening danger.

Folklore may not tell us the "scientific" truths of our time, but it tells
us better than almost any other form of human expression about our
"feeling truths." It might seem to us that we have always known what
things are "good" or "bad." Actually, we have been carefully taught

"Mowgli," © *The Walt Disney Company.*

by our culture. That is the nature of folklore. Rather than being what is "not true," or far from our lives, folklore is with us every moment of the day, in our unspoken assumptions as well as in our most eloquent proverbs and legends. It consists of traditions we have learned from the culture in which we grew up and into which we grow. In our folklore we find expression of our deepest feelings, including the way we see ourselves in relation to our environment.

It appears that the closer human culture has been to the life patterns of the wolf, the more respected the animal has been. Thus, when humans were hunters, they admired the wolf. They regarded it as exemplary, even human or divine. This attitude persists among people who value harmony with the natural elements on this planet. However, when some hunters became farmers, the wolf could no longer remain a respected co-hunter; rather, the wolf came to be a concrete threat to human life (and livestock). As humans encroached on the wolf's territory, making farmland of forest, the wolf became a symbol of predation on people's property.

Traditional symbols are compelling and ever-present. More than likely, they differ between cultures. The symbolism surrounding the wolf is no exception. Both among cultures, and even within a single culture such as that of "America," the symbol of the wolf is rich and varied. It acts upon us from within, generating fear, admiration, love, and often hostility. Where can we find this powerful symbolism better expressed than in our folk narratives, sayings, and general beliefs? It is no wonder that folk tales and proverbs about the wolf reveal a dizzying array of images. While scientists seek the "natural" wolf, the folklorist stalks the "symbolic wolf."

The Tales and Sayings

What does the hunt of the folklorist yield? What is the wolf like that we hear of in tales and proverbs? We find some wolves who for all the world seem to be and act like human beings. We find the nurturing wolf who raises abandoned children. We find the loyal and friendly wolf who rewards good deeds by humans. We find the intelligent wolf who can reason better, it seems, than can humans. We find the "dangerous" wolf, powerful and hungry, who at times eats to the point of gluttony. And we find the supernatural wolf who, in its most insidious incarnation, becomes the "evil" wolf, the dread werewolf who has a particular yen for human meals, especially of children.

As we search, we find that there are numerous international folktales in which the husband or the wife is an enchanted animal whose spell can be broken only by the spouse burning or somehow destroying the skin of the beast. When this is done, the human is at last set free of the enchantment. In these tales the husband or wife is often transformed into a wolf who changes into a human by day and an animal by night.

One of the most touching folk narratives which depicts the wolf as kin to man is a Menomini creation myth in which the wolf is literally a twin brother of the hero. It is the hero who names all the plants and animals of the world, and when he is finished with his task, he and his brother the wolf retire to live in a small dwelling on the edge of a large lake. The wolf hunts for his brother and they are content. However, the hero tells his brother the wolf that the evil beings who dwell in the lake wish him death and he warns the wolf never to cross that body of water. But after a long day's hunt, the wolf forgets, attempts to swim across to his home, and is destroyed by the lake spirits. His brother's mourning ripples across the earth, causing the hills to form and the valleys sink. When his brother, the wolf, returns as a "shade" to him, he tells him to go to the land of the dead and rule there. As is the fate of all mankind, in time they will meet again in that place.

Equally poignant as the "human" wolf is the animal who appears in one of the world's most widely spread legends: that of the wolf who nourishes and raises abandoned or lost children. The story of the wolf who suckled Romulus and Remus, legendary founders of the great city of Rome, is told in many forms in many cultures. Likewise we hear of the Irish king who was rescued as a baby by a wolf and grew to regain his rightful throne. Many cultures have stories of children raised by wolves, the most famous of which is perhaps, Mowgli, of Rudyard Kipling's *Jungle Books*. This compelling and widespread theme involves a she-wolf, in stark contrast to the majority of wolf narratives in which the wolf is a male.

But the wolf is not always this close to humans in the tales which depict him as the "good" wolf. He might simply be a friend or a grateful acquaintance—one who acts very much like a human being. The Japanese tell a tale of a brave youth who pulled a bone from the throat of a choking wolf. The story reminds us of one found in Aesop's fables. In the Japanese tale, the grateful wolf rewards the young man with a present of a large pheasant. To the dismay of the youth's friends, the wolf picks a night when they are all at a party, leaving the wolf to deliver the gift to the hero while his friends cower at the sight of the animal.

The Clever Wolf

Not only do many tales tell of wolves who are human-like, nurturing, and grateful, other tales reflect the animal as smart, wise, even more clever than humans. One Irish legend has it that a man set out one day to go from one town to another and purposely carried a sharp

"Reynard and Isegrim," by Fritz Eichenberg.

sword to fend off the attacks of the wolves who were known to frequent the road to the neighboring town. Three times a wolf attacked him, and three times he drove it off with his sword. Just as he came in sight of his destination, the man met a friend on the road, traveling to the town from which he had come. He saw that his friend was unarmed and so he gave him his sword. The town was not far off. Soon after they parted, his friend was accosted by the same wolf. The wolf, seeing the sword of the first man, immediately set off down the road in the opposite direction, overtaking and devouring the now unarmed owner of the sword. We do not know who first recounted the legend, but if wolves have their own folklore, that must certainly be one of their favorite tales. These narratives tell us about the intelligent wolf, the wolves about which the proverbs say: "You must cut down the woods to catch the wolf''; or ''Wolves lose their teeth, but not their memory.'' Such a narrative, if told in Russia, would make a good companion to the Russian saying ''The wolf is fed by his feet.''

But while some folk narratives show the wolf as a powerful and positive symbol, we also have tales which tell us about foolish wolves. One long complex German tale tells of how a fox outsmarted a wolf by showing him where there was honey in a beekeeper's cellar. Both wolf and fox squeezed through the small window to get in, but while the fox ate daintily, the wolf ''wolfed'' his honey. When the beekeeper heard the animals in the cellar, the fox could scamper out the window, while the bloated wolf was caught in the opening and received a mighty beating. That foolish wolf might well have been in the European tale of the seven wolves who wished to see over a wall. Since the wall was high, they had to climb on one another's backs to accomplish the task. However, the wolf at the bottom of the pile was an absent-minded fellow, and just as the final wolf was struggling to the top of the stack, he decided to walk off on some other business, leaving a tangled tumble of wolves behind.

Such tales tell us of wolves who have qualities we admire or can laugh at. However, there are also many tales that show the wolf as a powerful and dangerous animal. These tales are about the wolves one does not wish (as the proverb goes) ''to be thrown to.''

''Fenrir.''

23

The Wolf God

The embodiment of the powerful, dangerous wolf is found in the ancient Scandinavian myth of the wolf Fenrir. Fenrir was the illegitimate offspring of the no-account god Loki. He was a fierce and powerful animal, and he grew to a great size. The only god he trusted was the god of war, Tyr, who fed him daily. The gods saw that Fenrir was becoming unruly and so they decided he must be restrained. Not any ordinary rope or chain would contain him, so they made one, thin as a strand of spider's web, fabricated from all the unseen mysteries of earth: the roots of mountains, the sounds of fish breathing, the noise cats make when they walk. But Fenrir would not be bound unless one god placed his hand in his mouth. Tyr, his friend, was the only one to sacrifice himself, and to this day he is depicted with only one hand. Fenrir was bound, but it is believed by some that one day he will break his bonds; his jaws will be so mighty and wide that he will swallow the earth, the sky, the moon, the gods, and a new world will emerge from the ruins.

Fenrir is indeed the embodiment of the dangerous and powerful wolf. But in numerous tales and legends we find the same qualities of the wolf highlighted with the animal in a more "natural" form. In *My Antonia* Willa Cather recounts a widespread legend in which an enormous pack of wolves attacks a series of sleighs returning from a festive wedding party one bitter cold night in Russia. The only survivors of the carnage are the two drivers of the lead sleigh who throw the bride and groom to the wolves in order to lighten their load and reach town alive. Eventually they are exiled from Russia for this deed, and in the novel we find one of them, now old and feeble, dying in their little shack on the Nebraska prairie. As he is dying he hears the howls of the prairie coyotes and mistakes them for the voices of those wolves that horrid night long ago. And so he dies, hearing the cries of the dying wedding revelers, and the howling of the rapacious wolves of his memory.

Tales of Warning

It is a small step to take from the dangerous, powerful, wolf to that of the plundering and gluttonous wolf. Indeed, one of our best known fairy tales tells of "Little Red Riding Hood" and a wolf who was not only powerful and smart, but rapacious. The sexual overtones of the story are often overlooked, but it is perhaps one of the most important cautionary tales taught to children in Western culture. The wolf is one of the very few animals who, especially when associated with danger,

---

"Little Red Riding Hood and the Wolf," by Paul Gustave Doré, circa 1860.

is endowed with not only life-threatening power, but sexually threatening power as well. Another popular cautionary tale tells us how to plan our lives to "keep the wolf from the door." The "Three Little Pigs" contend with a wolf who is hardly friendly, and quite hungry. Not knowing how to build one's house is indeed life-threatening. The French have a proverbial saying for someone who is always hungry: *manger comme un loup* [he eats like a wolf]. Stories about wolves with excessive appetites tell us much about the dangers in our society of too much craving or too little "common sense."

And so we have known human-like wolves, both dangerous and friendly. But when the ingredient of "sin" entered the picture, and it was combined with the power of the wolf, the animal became not just dangerous, but evil. Thus in the witch trials in the late Middle Ages, the werewolf was seen as the devil's servant. The many tales of enchanted husbands and wives who "shape shifted" from human to wolf form, still were told, but they were, and still are, overshadowed by the shape-shifting from human to evil wolf. Earlier, such shifts were not seen as necessarily evil, just supernatural. But as the natural wolf came to be associated with the evil "werewolf," wolves came to be called "the Devil's dogs." It has been impossible for the wolf to shake the association, even though we still tell many positive wolf stories. The Italians have a current saying: "The wolf can change his coat but not his vices," while the English have one "The wolf must die in his own skin." We may not realize it, but we have not forgotten about shape-shifting and we have connected it with the evil wolf. Ironically, the same theme found in the touching stories of the human lover in wolf form reaches from one end of the spectrum of symbolism to the other and manifests itself in tales about the werewolf, the evil wolf in human form, the beast in us. Our folklore tells us much.

In Homer (800 B.C.) we find the image of the wolf and the lamb as enemies. In the Bible we find the same image, but now the lamb symbolizes Christ, or Good, and the wolf symbolizes the Devil, or Evil. Such images, once amplified by social circumstance, as in the witch trials of the 17th century, are difficult to change. And even today we think, at least in part of our mind, of the wolf as evil. No matter how many other symbols of the wolf we carry, if we have been raised in European-American culture, the complex symbols are there. An old English proverb goes, "The wolf doth something every week that keeps him from church on Sunday."

We admire and even feel a kinship with the wolf who raised so many of those abandoned children. We may laugh at "the gray fool" as the Russians sometimes call the wolf. But when we are alone on a dark night, walking through a forest, the howl of a wolf will still be a chilling sound. It takes much learning to unlearn such deep set lessons.

But wait, have you ever wondered why we don't sing "Who's afraid of the big bad bear"? After all, the alliteration is so much more effective, and bears have done more documented damage to humans than have wolves. But symbols have their power, and that power rests in our minds and feelings so strongly influenced by our culture. There is no need to abandon symbols, even if we could. But it would be heartening if we only could remember that there is an animal out there, one which is flesh and blood, one which must be understood to be as much a part of our precious, fragile world as any other living thing.

Ellen Stekert, Ph.D., is a professor of folklore and English at the University of Minnesota. She has published, lectured, and performed widely in the fields of folklore and folk music, has served in such administrative positions as president of the American Folklore Society, and has taught at several major American universities.

JUDITH LEVIN

Children's Literature

L iterature written especially for children is a relatively new
historical development. There was no children's literature, just
as there were no children's clothing styles, until the early 1700s. Until
that time children older than babies were treated as miniature adults,
and many of the older fables and fairy tales that we now think of as
children's tales were originally enjoyed by adults and children alike.
Much of the earliest children's literature consists of morality tales,
designed to frighten children into behaving properly by showing them
the terrible consequences of wrong-doing. The stories tell of children
who burn up, drown, or are eaten by wild animals because they tell
lies or otherwise disobey their parents. More recent children's books
are—sometimes—less obviously moralistic, yet many authors are still
intent on teaching "correct" human behavior.

A brief historical survey of wolf imagery in children's literature can
tell us what image of the wolf authors wanted children to have, or at
least what images the authors had. The literature also reveals changing attitudes about the human place in the natural order. People writing
about wolves have often noted that the wolf is a powerful symbol of
nature, a kind of cultural Rorschach test in the sense that people pro-

"Child Feeding a Wolf," by David McPhail, 1981.

ject onto the animal their deepest feelings about nature. Thus, if authors believe that humans are engaged in a struggle against nature, the wolf is seen as an enemy; if they believe that humans are—or should be—in harmony with nature, the wolf is more likely seen as noble or kind. In other words, children's books about wolves are seldom *only* about wolves. They are also about the relationship of humans to each other and to the natural world.

The earliest children's-book wolves are bad tempered and dangerous or, at best, examples of how not to behave. For instance, in *Vice in its Proper Shape*, published around 1800, children become the animals whose vices they share: Master Greedyguts becomes a pig; Master Tommy Filtch, the thief, becomes a wolf. Although fairy tales were not considered suitable for children until the 19th century, it is not difficult to see "Little Red Riding Hood" as part of this tradition of moral tales, especially when we remember that in the earlier versions of the tale, the girl and her grandmother are not rescued. The "Three Little Pigs" and "The Boy Who Cried Wolf" are also tales about the nature of good or wise behavior, with the wolf functioning as a convenient bogeyman, the big toothy monster who will eat up children who stray.

Spare the Threat

Just as most modern psychologists no longer believe that "sparing the rod" will "spoil the child," modern children's books use fewer threats to teach cultural norms to children. While the traditional tales continue to be reprinted—in fact, these stories are the ones most people know best—both stories and illustrations are often modified to make them less frightening. Little Red Riding Hood is rescued; and the red-mouthed, sharp-toothed, hungry-looking wolf of older illlustrations is replaced by a smaller, gentler one. Scary wolves still exist, but they are a minority.

Some of the newer stories depend on our recognition of the stereotypical big bad wolf, but then undermine that image. Especially in the books for small children, we find wolves who try to be fierce and dangerous, but who are outsmarted, or even made fools of, by the children and little pigs they pursue. Other stories show a wicked wolf who reforms when someone tries to understand him. This sort of wolf is a victim of circumstances who "never had no opportunities," as one of them explains plaintively.

The consensus of modern children's books is, on the whole, that wolves are not really a threat. Some must be outsmarted, some need to "learn their lesson," but most are naturally kind, or will learn to be kind if given a chance. Many behave nobly, rescuing an injured woodsman in one story, helping lost children or abandoned babies in

Top: "Cuthbert," by James Marshall, 1977.
Bottom: "Walter," by Kelly Oechsli, 1975.

many others. What all these books have in common is that their messages have less to do with the nature of wolf behavior than with what constitutes proper behavior for humans. This is obvious in "Little Red Riding Hood," but equally true in the other tales. The books in which the helpless (piglets, small children) outsmart wolves are lessons in self-reliance and inventiveness; stories in which wolves are reformed suggest that societal circumstances or expectations create wickedness. The rescued woodsman tells the animals (who have shunned the wolf because of his skill as a hunter): "We all have good things in us and today Great Wolf has had the opportunity to show us how really great he is," the implication being that greatness lies in helping others, not in being a "great hunter." Since wolves would starve to death if they were not "great hunters," it seems reasonable to assume that this story is more concerned with human morality than with animal behavior.

Books written for older children show a number of different attitudes toward the wolf and toward the place of humans in the natural order. In some books written in the last 25-30 years but set on the 18th or 19th century American frontier, wolves threaten livestock or humans. The stories generally involve male adolescents hunting down or fighting off wolves. The boy proves himself to be an adult by fighting for the social and economic order against the wild, and manhood is equated with physical mastery over nature. The wolf is hated and feared, and is very much the fairy tale "big bad wolf." An exception among these frontier tales is Laura Ingalls Wilder's "Little House" series. In these books wolves appear as huge beasts traveling in enormous packs, chasing men on horseback or ringing the settlers' houses and howling. But Laura, the heroine, likes the wolves and they do not hurt her, which demonstrates her at-home-ness in the wilderness and distinguishes her from the other women of her family, whose dislike of the frontier manifests itself in a hatred of the wolves. Again, wolves embody the wilderness, here both frightening and exciting.

Man vs. Nature

In another group of books, written early in this century, there is again the concern with human power over nature and thus over the wolf, but the notion of mastery is more subtle. Jack London, Joseph Lippincott, and others are fascinated by the wolf's power and ferocity. The wolf is a foe, but a noble foe which men seek out to test their own courage. Here, too, men conquer nature and the wild, but they do so not by killing, as animals do, but by taming—socializing, domesticating—this most wild of animals.

In these examples of "man against the wild," humans are depicted as superior to animals. This superiority is also assumed by the authors of the early tales of feral children (children raised by wild animals, often by wolves) or in tales of wolves raised by humans. In the usual feral-child story—Kipling's *Jungle Book* is one many people know—the wolf-mother recognizes something cub-like and helpless about a lost baby and adopts it. As the child grows, he or she becomes more human, and must return to humankind, while maintaining a sense of kinship with the wolves. In many stories, and not only the feral-child stories, children, especially Indian, Eskimo, and black children, have a greater affinity for nature and the wild than do adults, especially Anglo adults. This pattern reflects an underlying cultural attitude which says that children and more "primitive" cultures are "closer to nature" than are white adults. According to this view, becoming an adult means outgrowing the wolves' world and moving into a more complex, "superior" human world.

Some of the newer books for children differ from the older ones in two related ways: the wolf still stands for nature, but the authors are less and less convinced of the superiority of humankind; also they are increasingly interested in educating their readers about wolves, even in novels. While some of the authors portray distorted and romanticized images of nature, others are well-read in wolf biology or are themselves naturalists or biologists. These authors emphasize different wolf traits than London and Lippincott. The emphasis in the newer books is on the social and familial relations of the wolves, which are admired for their social co-operation, not their fierceness. For example, in the Newberry-award-winning *Julie of the Wolves*, an Eskimo girl is adopted by wolves. However, instead of the mysterious wolf/child affinity which usually causes wolves to adopt stray babies, Julie is accepted because she observes wolf society, rather like an anthropologist studying a foreign culture. She learns to read wolf body language, and to communicate with the wolves. Rather than Julie's making the wolves conform to human behavior, she learns to conform to wolf behavior. This reversal of the earlier pattern is characteristic of many of the newer children's books about wolves. Instead of wild wolves who must be shot or trapped, or who must conform to human standards of domesticity, it is the humans who must understand the wolves. In *Julie of the Wolves* cowards kill the wolves, again reversing an earlier pattern in which killing or overcoming a wolf demonstrates the greatest possible bravery. Some of the newer books are even written from the point of view of the wolves, and when the pack is slaughtered by hunters in airplanes, the reader feels attacked, identifying with the wolves, not with the humans.

Like "Little Red Riding Hood," the current pro-wolf books teach "correct" human behavior, but the notions of correct behavior have changed. Older morality tales taught children to listen to their parents and not to speak to strangers, and the "frontier" books taught that humans and nature are in competition; these newer books reappraise the human place in the natural order. In the earlier books, wolves threaten the social order and humans must maintain it; now it is humans who endanger the natural order, often showing themselves to be less compassionate and less wise than the wolves they kill. Humans rather than wolves are shown to be greedy bloodthirsty killers.

Children's books are designed to teach as well as to entertain, and many of the current books emphasize the need to preserve and defend the wolf. But this does not mean that the earlier images no longer exist. When I spoke to children and adults about wolves in children's books, many were familiar with only one image: the big bad wolf of "Little Red Riding Hood" and "The Three Little Pigs." Yet modern children also have other images of the wolf, gleaned from television, movies, books, and folklore. Thus a survey of wolf imagery in children's literature reveals our own changing attitudes about suitable child behavior, and about wolf-human relationships. The big bad wolf of folklore is clearly not yet dead or pardoned, but at least his more amiable descendants are beginning to erase his criminal record.

Judith Levin is a Ph.D. candidate in folklore at the University of Pennsylvania, Philadelphia. She teaches folklore and English composition at the University of Pennsylvania and Temple University, and lectures on folklore in children's literature.

F rom Judith Levin's essay we have learned some of the things adults tell children about wolves. Now we have a collection of drawings which show us what wolves look like as seen through children's eyes. Several elementary teachers encouraged their students to draw pictures of wolves, both before and after the students had seen the *Wolves and Humans* exhibit in Boise, Idaho. The pictures speak for themselves:

36

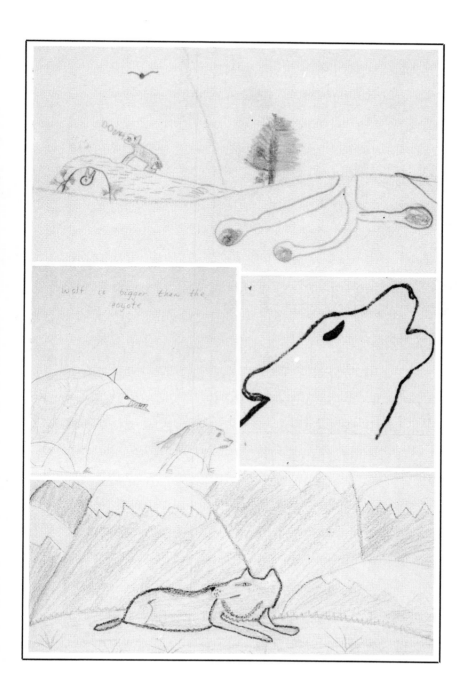

37

Indian Legends

O ut of respect for our continent's First People we will begin in their way, with a prayer. Watch Blue Horse, an old Lakota warrior who learned to hunt from wolves. He knows their dawn song and sings it each morning, not with head bowed but with hands aloft and head high. He sings without drum, in the language of Wolf. Then he calls to the West wind, which to his people is the direction of the wolf—"The West is where we belong, the Wolves and I, and my old friends now dead. May we meet again on the Other Side."

This picture of Blue Horse was recorded by Natalie Curtis in 1906, while a few wolves still remained on the great Plains. It tells us of the respect between equally competent hunters, a respect typical of the people who crossed the Bering Strait to become this continent's Native Americans.

Humans and wolves survived in this land because they were resourceful and because each was independent yet willing to help those less able among them. Native Americans, as they spread into widely differing climates and conditions, learned how to live from all creatures, from bird and darting mouse to those seemingly without enemy but man—wolf, eagle, badger, bear. The Indian people saw that each

"Buffalo Hunt Under the Wolf Skin Mask," by George Catlin, 1832-33.

animal, no matter how small, had an important place on this earth and had lessons to teach us. Nature was their authority and their great book; they learned not from professors or classrooms but from observation.

Eagle Chief, a Pawnee of the Bear Society, once explained to Curtis, "In the beginning of all things, wisdom and knowledge were with the animals, for Tirawa, the One Above, did not speak directly to man. Tirawa spoke to man through his works and the Pawnee understands the heavens, the beasts, and the plants." When Pawnee buffalo hunters watched wolves they saw hunters like themselves, with skill and endurance, showing ferocity against prey or foe, ably defending their territory against invasion.

The first lesson of the wolf, for the Plains people, was two-fold: how to hunt with quiet cunning, and how to share the spoils with the pack. Plenty-Coups, chief of the Crow in Montana's Yellowstone River coun-

"Wolf Skin Headdress."

try, once described to historian Frank Linderman the way he and other boys of his tribe were taught to hunt like wolves. Says Plenty-Coups, an older relative gathered village boys each morning, "Off would go our shirts and leggings. There was no talking, no laughing, but only carefully suppressed excitement while our teacher painted our bodies with the mud that was sure to be there. He made ears of it and set them on our heads, so that they were like the ears of wolves." The boys dropped to their knees and "our teacher would cover our backs with the wolf skins we had stolen out of our fathers' lodges. Ho! Now we were a real party of Crow Wolves and anxious to be off."

Slipping quietly through camp, stealing and then sharing bits of meat taken from the drying racks of aunts and grandmothers, swimming in ice-cold creek water, learning to be tough and clever as the wolf, the

40

boys prepared for their first bow and their first antelope hunt, which would come soon.

Another prairie people, the Blackfoot, were aware of the constant presence of wolves. George Bird Grinnell spent several years observing and recording their lives beginning in the 1890's, before the prairies were plowed. He says that the presence of wolves in those days was interpreted as opportunity rather than danger. Wolves were considered to be great friends, traveling beside the Pawnee, barking and howling as a way of communicating about the game which both man and wolf sought. Men would call out, "No, I will not give you my body to eat, but I will give you the body of some one else, if you will go along with us." Then the People would watch and learn where to find game as they shared food with the wolves.

Often the wisdom of the wolf was passed from one generation to another by means of stories. Anna Lee Townsend, one of the Shoshone-Bannock people of Idaho, says of her people, "There was a story for everything our people did; whether they sang, danced, prayed, hunted, built a fire, or went to war; every act of their daily lives had its own tradition." From Alaska to the central Plains, from the Pacific Northwest coast to the edge of the Eastern Woodlands, wolf tales are plentiful and show us what could be learned from this great and powerful animal.

Coyote and Wolf

Often, Wolf teaches the way to live by example. The northern Paiute of Idaho suggest the right way to hunt by a contrast between the conscientious Wolf and foolish, impulsive Coyote. Native Americans, like other hunting people around the world, frequently tell stories of a Keeper of the Animals who gives his people what game they need as long as none is wasted; here it is Wolf who keeps all the game of that country in a cave and brings out one at a time, only what can be eaten each day. Coyote, the impatient one, pesters his older brother until Wolf tells him the secret of the cave and Coyote finds it. Now he must lift the skin on the door only a crack, enough for one animal. But at the sight of all those elk, buffalo and deer, Coyote is excited and forgets himself. The cave opening gapes as wide as Coyote's drooling mouth. All the animals pound out of the cave in a crush of hooves and dust. Coyote shoots, but hits nothing. Too late now, he rushes about, shouting to the few remaining deer, trying to herd them back into the cave. One tiny deer quivers behind a shrub; Coyote triumphantly draws his bow and shoots it, just as Wolf approaches.

But Coyote is not discouraged. He proudly serves his deer to Wolf, then says, "Well, it looks like the animals have found new homes. How can we hunt them now?"

Wolf, of course, has magical powers. "I put sagebrush into piles," he says. "Soon the piles fill with rabbits." Wolf tells Coyote how to hunt groundhogs, also, thinking these are so slow even Coyote can catch them. But he knows his brother too well, and warns Coyote against becoming careless and letting the Indians catch him as he hunts.

Coyote remembers his instructions for a few minutes. He heaps sagebrush into big piles; soon they are full of rabbits. But Coyote is so hungry that instead of killing the rabbits and taking them home to share as his brother Wolf would do, Coyote eats them all, on the spot. "I can pile the sage and catch more rabbits," he tells himself.

Now like many a foolish younger brother, when Coyote's stomach is full he wants to play, not work. He is seen by the Indians, pursued, and only Wolf can protect him. Again due to Coyote's carelessness in the battle, Wolf is killed. Poor Coyote must spend years gaining the discipline and the resources to take revenge and bring home his brother's remains so that Wolf can return to life.

The contrast between Wolf, who learns from his mistakes, and ever-foolish Coyote is a favorite one among native storytellers—perhaps because Coyote is suspiciously like humankind.

Both the wisdom and endurance of Wolf are celebrated in the Arikara explanation for the creation of earth in its present state. Here, Wolf and man are brothers and companions, together responsible for earth's present state. Cottie Burland tells the story in her book of North American mythology.

The Creation of the World

In the beginning, they say, was water and sky. Here on high you could find Nesaru the sky spirit, and Wolf and Lucky-man. Below lay a watery vastness, empty, it seemed, with only two small ducks swimming about, making eternal, small ripples. Envisioning another kind of earth, with space and variety for myriad creatures,

Wolf and Lucky-man asked the ducks to dive down for mud. Using his endless energy, Wolf took half of the mud to build a great prairie for hunting beasts like himself. Lucky-man, his partner in creation, built hills and valleys where the Indians could hunt and live. Last they pushed up the remaining mud into banks of a river, which you can still see, to divide their territories.

Earth was ready. Wolf and Lucky-man understood that large creatures must emerge from the reproduction of smaller, humble ones. They enter deep into the earth to find two Spiders who are meant to begin propogating the world. Imagine their disgust when they find the Spiders to be not only ignorant of the business of reproduction, but so dirty and ugly that they aren't interested in each other. Wolf and Lucky-man scrub down their charges and explain the pleasures and responsibilities of fertilization. Clean and enlightened, the Spiders give birth to earth's many creatures—the eight-legged like themselves, the six, the four, and finally the two-legged ones.

Heroes in Native American stories, even those like Wolf who are smart enough and strong enough to be part of earth's formation, still have frailties and personal quirks, just like the rest of us. Stories are told to suggest that even the noblest among us can suffer the penalties waiting for the vain and greedy. Many tales tell how brave but overconfident ones are tricked, conquered by much smaller, seemingly insignificant creatures. Wolf suffers such a fate at the hand of Chickadee in a story of the Okanagans of the Pacific Northwest. This version, one of many, is told by Mourning Dove, an itinerant farm worker who saved a number of the stories of her people in the 1930's.

Chickadee and the Shoo-Mesh Bow

Chickadee aspires to make a shoo-mesh bow, a magic bow of great powers. But such a bow must be made from the bones of the mighty elk, which would be enough of a task for such a tiny bird; to make matters worse, an elk is quickly found by Wolf, who would seem to be more than a match for the little bird.

Chickadee flatters Elk into offering a ride across the river. Then by distracting Elk as he uses his little flint knife, Chickadee manages to kill his huge victim. Chickadee works quickly; he has just finished skinning Elk when Mother Wolf finds him. Wolf spies the meat and runs for her children to help her steal it from Chickadee, who pretends to be willing to share. But while Mother Wolf seeks out her young, Chickadee has carried the meat to a high cliff and built a fire. Before the wolves can reach him, Chickadee wraps white-hot stones in strips of elk fat and says, "No need to climb these rocks, Mother. I will throw a mouthful of meat to each of you." The greedy wolves open their mouths wide; Chickadee drops a hot rock into each gaping mouth and kills them.

Stories like these are called cautionary tales; behind them is the assumption that the listener can learn from the mistakes and the instruction of others. So also the wolf. Barry Lopez tells us that the Nunamiut hunters of Alaska, who watch wolf behavior closely, pay no attention to young wolves because "yearlings are always fooling around."

Wolf has other gifts for those who listen. One way the Plains people taught each other the right way to live was through the Medicine Wheel. Medicine means much more than something you ingest to make you well; it is a way of seeing which brings you power while it puts you in the right relationship with the rest of creation. Hyemeyohsts Storm has returned from the Teachers among his people, the Plains Indians of Montana. He relates stories around the Medicine Wheel in his book, **Seven Arrows**. Each point on the wheel represents a point of view, a way of seeing and experiencing which is signified by a particular animal. Our goal should be first to know our personal style or way of seeing, then to travel around the wheel, see our life from other perspectives. Wolf, with his endurance and caring for his family, is found at one of the points, associated also with the clouds or wind. The young, seeking guidance and knowledge of themselves, take a journey in quest of a vision and a guiding spirit to assist them; those who choose Wolf as their particular Spirit will be lucky; but all can be stronger and wiser by seeing from Wolf's point of view.

Often this relationship between Indian and Wolf is acted out in ceremonies, not all of them serious. The Cheyenne animal dance, observed in 1923 by George Bird Grinnell, is a time for foolery. The women build a pen of stakes and brush; each man who has been given a dance from some animal in a dream organizes a group of friends to dress as that animal. The first two dancers are wolves. They are joined by men taking the parts of buffalo, elk, deer, bear, coyote—all creatures which the Cheyenne cannot corral easily. Now the best warriors come along, clowning, doing everything backwards as the "animals" trot about. It is a ceremony which rejoins men to the animal spirits which guide them.

Wolf is not always a hero or friend. Agricultural, pastoral people, hovering over their fat, domestic animals fear the gray forms lurking at forest's edge. Among the Navajo and Hopi, one herding sheep and goats, the other farming small plots near their pueblos, the wolf has a dual personality. Remnants of an earlier respect can be found in public and private religious ceremonies and in a few tales. Small carvings of various animals, called fetishes, are used at altars; wolves are among them. And the Katchinas, those costumed dancers who represent the many sacred powers of the universe, include Wolf. Having Wolf-Katchina dance beside Sheep in the Hopi mountain sheep dance is a recognition of the part which Wolf plays in the harmonious workings of nature.

The Navajo, too, include the power-filled Wolf in one of their most important healing ceremonies. Even today, the best way to heal illness, among the Navajo, is to hire a healer who will arrange a four or five

"Nature Cycle," by Gary Meeches.

day ceremony. This healer knows the long, complex songs which will unite the sick one with the community and with the distant Sacred Powers which can bring back peace and harmony. These songs or chants tell stories of how the Powers have, at other times, saved the Navajo people. One of the most important, the Bead Way ceremony, describes Wolf as a benevolent hunter who helps Bead Boy return home safely from the sky kingdom. The event is celebrated in a sand painting, "Exchange of quivers," which depicts Wolf, Mountain Lion, Spotted Lion, Bobcat, Lynx and Badger all offering their powers to Bead Boy.

In daily life, however, and in popular folklore, the wolf has a fearful association. Both Navajo and Hopi believe that witches travel in the form of wolves. Those same Powers, which can be beneficial, can be abused and used to harm other people; and so it is commonly believed that witches use the wolf's spirit powers maliciously.

These evil ones gather for meetings, one schoolboy told anthropologist Clyde Kluckhohn, to plan trouble and to initiate new recruits. Curiosity can be dangerous—"If the Navajo Wolf catches you at the meeting they bring you inside and ask you if you want to learn or die. If you want to learn, they bring you inside and say, 'Who do you want, your sister or brudder?' If you say brudder, two days after that he will die . . . It is like paying to learn, only you don't pay in money. You have to pay with your brudder or sister."

Like evil ones everywhere, Navajo witch wolves are believed to have remarkable powers—to travel almost instantly, to have heightened powers of sight, smell, and intelligence. The exploits of these wolf-witches sound more like those of bad guys in contemporary folklore than like real wolves. Wolf-witches in these stories are vicious loners willing to pay for their initiation into witch-dom with the lives of family members. In actual wolf packs, as we know, family members are always defended and protected.

In a similar vein, recent collectors of stories among the Menomini have heard tales borrowed from European folktales, which put Wolf in the position of fool. In one, for instance, Fox is the good hunter who brings home game, while Wolf is the greedy one who is tricked into hanging his tail over a hole in the ice so fish will bite it. In other places, Wolf simply retreats, as in a Wasco story recorded by Lucullus McWhorter, where Coyote tricks Wolf and his brothers into climbing up into the sky. Coyote sneaks down and destroys the arrow path behind him, leaving the wolves stranded but forever decorative in the night sky.

It is true, Wolf has retreated and is part of a past that cannot be recaptured, one more of the Ancestors described in a poem by Grey Cohoe:

In the days of peaceful moods,
　they wandered and hunted.
In the days of need or greed,
　they warred and loafed.
Beneath the lazy sun, kind winds above,
　they laughed and feasted.
Through the starlit night, under the moon,
　they dreamed and loved.
Now, from the wind-beaten plains,
　only their dust rises.

Not all is lost. We have left behind the time of Sitting Bull's surrender speech when he said of the Sioux, "They are neither red warriors nor white farmers. They are neither wolf nor dog." Now we know that all the earth is sacred, that we are all brother to wolf and dog, to fellow creatures tame and wild. We must join in the prayer of Lololomai, Hopi chief of the village of Oraibi, as recorded by Natalie Curtis: Curtis:

> He goes to the edge of the cliff and turns his face to the rising sun, and scatters the sacred corn meal. Then he prays for all the people. He asks that we may have rain and corn and melons, and that our fields may bring us plenty. But these are not the only things he prays for. He prays for everybody in the whole world—for everybody. And not people alone; Lololomai prays for all the animals. And not animals alone; Lololomai prays for all the plants. He prays for everything that has life. That is how Lololomai prays.

Jeanette Ross is a free-lance writer and educator in Boise, Idaho. She holds an M.A. in English and an Ed.D. in education. In addition to her non-fiction writing, Ross is the author of **K Ranch**, *a novel of contemporary Montana.*

JAMES A. NEE AND GLENN OAKLEY

Wolf Management

T he Indian belief that people can coexist in harmony with wolves
has only recently begun to be accepted by the white American
public. That desire to once again have wolves roaming America's wild
country carries with it a host of biological and political problems.

The truism that it is easier to break something than it is to fix it holds
for wolves as well as machinery. Biologists and land managers are faced with more than the problem of how to bring back wolves to an area.
They are simultaneously faced with the question of where to encourage
wolf populations, how many wolves should be in any given area, and
what should be done if these wolves harm livestock.

Such questions quickly leap from the biological to the political. Many
ranchers in potential wolf habitat fear the reestablishment of wolves.
Some hunters view wolves as unneeded competitors for big game like
deer, elk, and moose. And some citizens hold an innate fear of the
animals. Will their children be safe in the national parks if wolf parks
are reintroduced, some wonder.

The U.S. Fish and Wildlife Service, a branch of the Department of
Interior, is the agency charged with overseeing and ensuring the
reestablishment of wolves. Wolf reestablishment is more than a policy

---

"National Elk Refuge, Jackson Hole, Wyoming," by John Wilbrecht.

decision by this single department; it is the legal mandate of the Endangered Species Act.

In cooperation with state wildlife agencies and private groups, the department is attempting to develop and manage wolf populations in northern Minnesota, Yellowstone National Park, the Glacier National Park region of northern Montana, and the mountainous wilderness country of central Idaho. Wolves are not listed as endangered in Alaska, and are still killed—for sport, for fur, and to protect big game populations.

Northern Minnesota is home to an estimated 1,200 gray wolves, far more than in any other place in the lower 48 states. Here the wolf is listed as "threatened," which is a less critical designation than "endangered." In 1978 the Fish and Wildlife Service approved a state-federal plan that, if successful, will lead to the full recovery of the Minnesota wolf population (one wolf per 50 square miles) and its removal from the threatened species list.

Wolf Recovery

The plan for Minnesota wolves has six objectives:
1. managing the wolf indirectly by enhancing the habitat of white-tailed deer and other wolf prey;
2. conducting research on wolves to learn their abundance, distribution, and ecology;
3. providing law-enforcement to prevent the killing of wolves;
4. educating the public about wolf ecology;
5. providing the public with opportunities to comment on wolf management; and
6. using a zone management system to control wolves that kill livestock.

The zone system is considered critical for the coexistence of wolves and humans. It allocates certain areas or zones primarily for wolf use, sets aside a buffer zone, and then allocates a third zone as an area where wolves can exist only if they do not interfere with human activities.

In Zone I the wolf takes precedence over other users. Management decisions will favor the needs of the wolf when other land users pose threats to the wolf population.

In Zone II, the wolf is still important, but is not the primary user of an area. Management decisions—such as whether or how to log—will at least maintain the habitat conditions. Land use practices that harm the wolves can be allowed.

In Zone III wolves are not a primary management consideration. Any wolves killing livestock will be killed or removed.

The zone system, along with the other management measures such

"Blood Sampling of Tranquilized Wolf," by Patrick D. Kains.

as increasing deer populations and limiting road construction in wolf territory, appears to be working in Minnesota. There are more than 12,000 livestock operations in the 30,000 square miles of northern Minnesota wolf range. Yet between 1979 and 1984 only about 23 farms per year lost livestock to wolves. The total average annual losses were 3 cows, 18 calves, 50 sheep and 183 turkeys.

Wolf recovery in the West is directed by the Northern Rocky Mountain Wolf Recovery Team, comprised of 11 members from four federal agencies, three state agencies, the National Audubon Society, and a livestock organization. The team's still uncompleted recovery plan, patterned after the Minnesota plan, calls for establishment of wolf populations in Montana's Glacier Park and Bob Marshall Wilderness Area, the central Idaho wilderness, and Yellowstone Park. The team recommends adoption of the zone system to manage the wolves in these areas.

The Montana recovery area already has a small pack of wolves; the Idaho area has about a dozen scattered single wolves; and Yellowstone has no wolves at all. Each recovery region has an abundant population of wolf prey—elk and deer—a large amount of federal land, and sparse numbers of livestock. The recovery team's goal is to have ten breeding pairs of wolves in each of the three areas.

Natural wolf migration from Canada is the source for the present wolves in Montana and Idaho. Continued wolf migration is expected to re-populate the recovery areas in these states. This plan relies on wolves' inclination to disperse and populate new territory. If this biological trickle-down theory fails to establish wolf populations, then reintroduction by transplanting wolves from Canada will be considered.

The Yellowstone Plan

Transplanting wolves from Canada is the proposed plan for Yellowstone Park. The park is too far from Canada to be populated by migrating wolves. Wolves would be live-trapped from areas of British Columbia or Alberta where elk are the primary prey. Such wolves would have already developed the hunting behavior and techniques necessary for survival in the park.

The reintroduction plan has received strong support from the public, but faces equally strong opposition from livestock interests who fear wolf depredation on ranches surrounding the park. The recovery team believes that the zone system, by permitting the killing of problem wolves, would minimize wolf/livestock conflict. In addition, the team proposes monetary compensation to ranchers for wolf-killed livestock.

In the Yellowstone Park region, however, livestock losses are not considered a serious threat by biologists. The over-abundant elk, deer, moose, bison, and bighorn are expected to provide an ample prey base for the wolves. Without predators to cull the herds, the big game animals of the park have in many cases overpopulated, resulting in overgrazing of natural vegetation and consequent starvation of wildlife. Wolves will fill an empty ecological niche, actually benefitting the prey species.

In Alaska, where wolves are not protected by the Endangered Species Act, they are considered competitors for big game. In areas where human hunting pressure and wolf populations are both high, the Alaska Department of Fish and Game has instituted an aerial hunting program to thin the wolf population. This controversial management practice has been contested in the courts over the past decade.

Canada, too, continues to manage its wolf population with poison and guns. All Canadian provinces and territories in wolf range carry out wolf control programs to limit predation on livestock and huntable wildlife. Government trappers in British Columbia, Alberta, Manitoba, Saskatchewan, and the Yukon Territory use strychnine, cyanide, and Compound 1080 to kill wolves. Canadian law allows a property owner, such as a rancher, to kill wolves any time they damage his or her property. Similarly, the wolf is considered a furbearer in Canada and is pursued under liberal trapping and hunting seasons. Canadian authorities report that wolves are not threatened with extinction anywhere in the country.

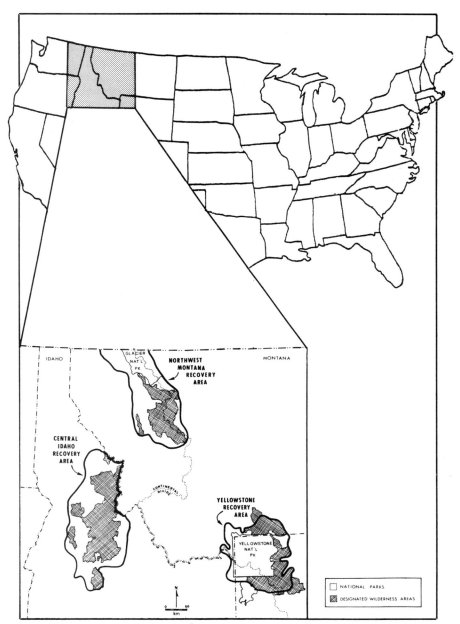

Wolf Recovery Area Map, by Robert Ream, 1986.

In many ways, wolf management is the same as big game management. If elk, deer and moose populations are strong and healthy, wolves should do well. Nevertheless, opposition to wolf recovery remains strong in many segments of society. Wolves are still illegally killed in the lower 48 states. Such poaching may be the primary obstacle to the natural reestablishment of wolves in Idaho and Montana by migration. Often, those who oppose wolf recovery and shoot wolves on sight have developed their opinions of the animals based on misconceptions derived from our folk tales and our history as a frontier people.

However misguided, political pressure combined with poaching has the potential to squelch wolf recovery in America.

Wolf management is thus ultimately a public issue, and public education about wolves may have more to do with their survival than all the recovery plans in the world. Biologists are betting that the more we know about wolves, the more we will want to protect them and ensure their survival.

James Nee is an ecologist with 18 years of experience with the U.S. Fish and Wildlife Service. He is stationed in Boise, Idaho. He has Master's degrees in zoology and public administration.

Further Reading

Botkin, B.A. 1984. *A Treasury of American Folklore*. Crown Publ., N.Y.

Burland, Cottie. 1985. *North American Indian Mythology*, rev. ed. P. Bedrick Bks., N.Y.

Clark, Ella E. 1953. *Indian Legends of the Pacific Northwest*. University of California, Berkeley.

Dixon, Paige. 1973. *Silver Wolf: a story of wilderness life*. Atheneum Press, N.Y.

Dorson, Richard M. 1978. *Folktales Told Round the World*. University of Chicago Press, Chicago.

Fox, Michael. 1973. *The Wolf*. Coward, McGann, the Geohegan, Inc., N.Y.

George, Jean C. 1972. *Julie of the Wolves*. Harper and Row, N.Y.

Grinnell, George Bird. 1962. *Blackfoot Lodge Tales*. University of Nebraska Press, Lincoln.

Lopez, Barry. 1979. *Of Wolves and Men*. Charles Scribner's Sons, N.Y.

Mech, L. David. 1970. *The Wolf: the ecology and behavior of an endangered species*. Natural History Press, Garden City, N.Y.

Mourning Dove. 1933. *Coyote Stories*. AMS Press, N.Y.

Passmore, John. 1978. *Man's Responsibility for Nature: ecological problems and Western traditions*. Macmillan, N.Y.

Robbins, Jim. 1986. "Wolves across the border." *Natural History*, Vol. 95, No. 5, pp. 6-15.

Thompson, Stith. 1966. *Tales of the North American Indians*. Indiana University Press, Bloomington.

Acknowledgments

This volume was sponsored by the Idaho Humanities Council

with added contributions from:

Defenders of Wildlife (who also sponsored the *Wolves and Humans* exhibit in Yellowstone National Park and in Boise, Idaho)

Ada County Fish and Game
League, Boise, Idaho

The Wildlife Society, Idaho Chapter

Craig Groves, Boise, Idaho

Jay Gore, Boise, Idaho

Cover Photograph By Layne Kennedy

Photo Illustration Credits